STACCATO SCRIPTS

A DAY IN THE MIND OF TICH OLDFIELD

Alan England

ERNIE'S INCREDIBLE ILLUCINATIONS

Alan Ayckbourn

Series Editors: Kate Harris and John Mannion
Support Material: Catherine Hodgetts
and Max Turton

Stanley Thornes (Publishers) Ltd

First published in 1991 by:
Stanley Thornes (Publishers) Ltd
Old Station Drive
Leckhampton
CHELTENHAM GL53 0DN
England

British Library Cataloguing in Publication Data

England, Alan
    A day in the mind of Tich Oldfield/Ernie's
    incredible illucinations. – (Staccato scripts)
    I. Title   II. Ayckbourn, Alan   III. Series
    822

    ISBN 0–7487–1168–6

ACKNOWLEDGEMENTS

The authors and publishers are grateful to the following for permission to reproduce extracts and photographs:

All-Sport UK Ltd page 53 ● Greenhills page 51 ● Hamish Hamilton *The Secret Life of Walter Mitty*, James Thurber ● London Features International Ltd pages 56, 57 ● Penguin Books Ltd *Supergran, Superstar* © Forrest Wilson (1982) ● 'Dreampoem' Roger McGough reprinted with permission of the Peter Fraser and Dunlop Group Ltd page 41 ● Sharp End Promotions Ltd page 58 ● Sporting Pictures UK Ltd page 56

The publishers have made every effort to contact copyright holders and apologise if any have been overlooked.

All applications to perform these plays, whether by amateurs or professionals, should be made to the author, c/o Stanley Thornes (Publishers) Ltd, Old Station Drive, Leckhampton, Cheltenham GL53 0DN.

Typeset by Tech-Set, Gateshead Tyne & Wear
Printed and bound in Great Britain at Ebenezer Baylis & Son Ltd
The Trinity Press, Worcester, and London

CONTENTS

A Day in the Mind of Tich Oldfield

CHARACTERS

Gooey Smiles
'Barrel' Snide
'Jammy' Chivers
Pam
Tich Oldfield
Father
Mother
'Thorny' Briar
Allman
Miss Feckless
Bus Driver
Zoo Keeper
Bimbo The Ape

Members of Tich's class, who become rioters, soldiers and plane passengers in Tich's mind.

PLAY ONE

Scene: Upstage, a boy, **'Tich' Oldfield,** *asleep in bed. Downstage, to one side, is a huge 'clapometer' looking like a thermometer with an indicator, and by it stands* **Pam,** *a girl of Tich's age, dressed in a bathing costume. Onto the downstage area, via some steps, dances an ebullient and unctuous compère,* **Gooey Smiles.**

Smiles   Thank you, ladies and gentlemen, thank you. This is your host, Gooey Smiles, and you are tuned in to your favourite talent show, *A Million to One.* We now come to the climax of the evening, the moment when *you* decide the fate of the brave and talented boys who have entertained us so wonderfully tonight. The clapometer will be registering your applause and the winner will receive the magnificent sum of one million pounds. As usual, I shall bring back each of the artists in turn to remind you of what they did, and first, if you remember, we had a youngster who wants to be a romantic pop singer, Darrel (known to his friends as 'Barrel') Snide!

(*Enter* **Barrel,** *a fat lad in a ridiculous outfit. He carries a guitar. His singing is hopelessly out of tune and the chords he strums are absolute guesswork. The actor can make the tune up as he goes along*)

Barrel   (*Singing*)

Every time I look into my mirror,
There's a face I always love to see.
I'm handsome and I'm clever,
I don't think I shall ever
Meet anyone as marvellous as me.

But, Pamelah! Oh, Pame-lah!
Let's both look in the mirror on the wall.
I'm as happy as can be
When you are next to me,
'Cos next to me I love you best of all.

(*As soon as he finishes,* **Pam** *raises a card on which is written 'BOO', thereby encouraging the audience to do this. The clapometer fails to move. Re-enter* **Smiles**)

Smiles   And the clapometer has registered nil, ladies and gentlemen, no points at all for Burbling Barrel, the Git with the Guitar. Never mind, Barrel, the competition is not over yet. Not by a long chalk. And speaking of chalk, we come to our next performer, ladies and gentlemen, and he was, if you recall, the tedious teacher from Oxford – or was it Cambridge? And here he is to offer you a date with boredom – 'Jammy' Chivers!

(*Exit* **Smiles** *and enter* **Chivers.** *He speaks with his teeth together and draws out his vowels. Horn-rimmed specs perch on the end of his nose*)

> **Chivers**   Enthralling events in History. In 55 BC, Julius Caesar landed, followed closely by Hengist and Horsa in 499 AD William the Conqueror landed in 1066 and the Magna Carta was signed in 1215. Simon de Montfort died in 1265 and in 1399 the Peasants revolted . . .

(*As though on cue,* **Pam** *raises a card marked 'SNORE' and the audience complies.* **Chivers** *carries on, blissfully ignorant*)

> Charles the First was executed in 1649, and the monarchy was restored in 1660. In 1788 George the Third went mad and in 1881 there was trouble with the Boers . . .

(*He pronounces it 'Boo-ers' and at this* **Pam** *raises the card marked 'BOO'. The audience responds limply.* **Smiles** *returns as* **Chivers** *steps to one side*)

> **Smiles**   Thank you, 'Jammy' Chivers, for that exhaustive, or should I say exhausting, list. And once again, ladies and gentlemen, the clapometer has registered a score of nil. No claps at all for Jammy the Jaw, and so far we have a dead heat – and I do mean dead. I think after that we could all do with a laugh, don't you? And who better to provide it than the mini-mimic from Yorkshire, the little lad with the great big talent, last but by no means least, David ('Tich') Oldfield!

(**Tich** *has risen from his bed, and he now comes downstage in his pyjamas.* **Smiles** *makes way for him.* **Tich** *embarks on a series of 'impressions' of famous people. They can be any that the actor is capable of attempting. After each one, there is laughter or sounds of appreciation. When he finishes,* **Pam** *raises a card marked 'CLAP' and there is volcanic applause. The indicator on the clapometer rockets to the top and shoots off into the air*)

> **Smiles**   (*Returning*) And we have a winner, ladies and gentlemen, and he has broken both the record and the clapometer. By your applause tonight, you have chosen the person you think should win the jackpot prize of one million pounds. And he is, of course, that inimitable imitator from the North, your friend and my friend, Tich Oldfield.

(*Solemn, regal music as* **Tich** *comes forward to shake hands with* **Smiles** *and receive his money*)

> **Smiles**   Congratulations, Tich, and here is your cheque for one million pounds. Don't drop it, will you, it might bounce. Haw! Haw! Haw! Seriously, though, what does it feel like to be rich, Tich? (*He smirks*)

> **Tich**   (*Also smirking*) Absolutely great, mate!

Smiles (*To audience*) Did you hear that? A natural wit as well. Is there no end to this boy's talents? Tell me, Tich, what are you going to do with the money?

Tich Spend it.

Smiles And very wise, too. Have you any idea what you'll spend it on?

Tich First thing I'm going to do is buy my parents a nice big house and a new car.

Smiles Now isn't that wonderful, ladies and gentlemen? His first thought is for the parents that brought him into the world, the father and mother who loved him and cared for him. Give him a big hand!

(*The audience applauds warmly*)

Will your parents be looking in, Tich? Would you like to say a few words to them?

Tich They're here.

Smiles They're in the audience? Well, why didn't you say so? Let's have them up, shall we? Mr and Mrs Oldfield, would you like to come onto the stage?

(**Father** *and* **Mother** *appear.* **Father** *shakes hands with the compère,* **Mother** *impulsively and tearfully embraces her son*)

Smiles (*With a tear in his voice*) Now isn't that a moving sight, ladies and gentlemen? A mother united with her loving son. (*He takes out a handkerchief. The audience weeps loudly*) I can understand your feelings, my dear friends. They do you credit, they really do. (*Snapping out of it*) And now, I'm sure you'd all like me to ask Mr Oldfield what he thinks of our talented victor.

Father (*Puzzled*) His name's David.

Smiles Eh? Oh, I see! The wit runs in the family. Haw! Haw! Haw! Mrs Oldfield, let's ask you, then. Are you proud of your son?

Mother I am that. He's one in a million.

Smiles In more senses than one, if you'll allow me to say so.

Father He's always been a credit to us.

Mother Never a bit of trouble. He's been a pleasure to bring up.

Smiles Now isn't that nice to hear? Model parents of a model son. The prize couldn't have gone to a more deserving family. Mr and Mrs Oldfield and Tich, it's been wonderful to make your acquaintance. Take your money and good luck to you.

(*The* **Oldfields** *leave the stage. Applause.* **Tich** *returns to bed and to sleep. The clapometer is removed*)

Well, it's time to bring our show to a close, ladies and gentlemen. We hope you've enjoyed it, and this is your host, Gooey Smiles, saying goodnight and sweet dreams!

(*He departs to appropriate music.* **Father** *and* **Mother** *bring on the breakfast table and two chairs for the next scene*)

(**Father** *sits at the table.* **Mother** *goes to the foot of the 'stairs'. She squawks like an angry duck*)

Mother   David! You David! Da-vid!

(**Tich** *stirs and answers sleepily*)

    Tich   I'm coming.

Mother   Shift yourself, will you? You'll be late for school again.

(**Tich** *gets out of bed and starts to dress*)

Mother   (*To* **Dad**) God help him when he starts work. They'll be sacking him before he clocks on.

  Father   Quite right, love. It's the likes of him we're fighting for, an' all.

Mother   Fighting! Is that what you call it? Sitting round on your backside all day?

  Father   But I'm on strike, Elsie.

Mother   I shall go on strike one of these days. Then you'd look sick, the lot of you.

(*Enter* **Tich**)

Mother   Why don't you come when you're called?

    Tich   I was dreaming.

Mother   Dreaming? You do nothing else. I wonder you bother to get up at all.

    Tich   I got woken up by a terry-dactyl.

Mother   Don't be so damned cheeky.

    Tich   (*Spotting his boiled egg*) It *was* a terry-dactyl. Look, it's left me a present.

(*He clouts it with his spoon*)

It's prehistoric, alright. I've bent me spoon.

Mother   That egg was fresh yesterday. Get it down you.

    Tich   Bird must have been constipated, then.

Mother It's all you'll get with your dad on strike.

Tich When are you going back, dad?

Father (*As though quoting*) When the employers are prepared to meet our demands.

Tich Why don't you just go and bash 'em up? There's a picture in our history books at school of a load of mill workers marching up to t'boss's house with clubs and the boss looking dead scared.

Father We don't do that anymore. Be in trouble wi' police. I like to keep my nose clean.

Tich Why don't you picket?

Father What, me nose?

Tich No, I mean why don't you be a picket? Stand at the gate and frighten scabs away.

Father That don't do any good. Best wait for t'representatives to negotiate a settlement.

Tich What does that mean?

Father Well . . . they talk.

Tich (*Scornfully*) Oh, talking.

Mother I'll give you talking. Haven't you started that egg, yet?

Tich I don't fancy it, mum.

Mother Well, you'll have to go without, then. I don't wonder they call you 'Tich'. You won't even be as big as your dad, and *he* daren't walk over a drain for fear of disappearing down it. Get off with you, or you'll miss that bus again.

Tich (*Standing*) Can I have twenty-five pence, dad?

Mother Twenty-five blasted pence? What for?

Tich It's school trip this afternoon. We're going to the zoo.

Mother Well you'll have to miss it, then, won't you? Do you think we've come into a fortune or something?

Tich I'll have to get it from the Poor Box, in that case.

Mother Get it from what?

Tich Poor Box. It's what they call the school fund. If your parents are too poor for you, they pay for you out of the school fund.

Mother You're not getting no money from no Poor Box. We'd never live it down. You're not taking no charity.

Father Go and get your school bag, lad. Things'll be better, soon.

(**Tich** *shrugs and goes upstairs.* **Mother** *brings a tray. She addresses* **Father**)

Mother Help me side this lot. Do something for a living.

Father (*Complying*) Seems a pity about the zoo.

Mother He's better off away from it. They'd only keep him there if he went. Pulling his blasted faces. (*They leave*)

(**Tich** *sits on his bed, hastily scribbling his homework*)

(*On comes* '**Thorny**' **Briar,** *brisk and breezy, head of Middle School. He stands behind the table as though it were a lectern*)

Briar And in conclusion, boys and girls, I'd like you to know that the Headmaster is very pleased with the way the three schools are coalescing. (*He tries again*) Are amalgamating. Becoming united. (*With vibrant drama*) Through our ancient corridors has blown a Wind of Change . . .

(*From offstage comes the sound of a rushing, mighty flatulence*)

Briar Who did that? WHO DID THAT? Oldfield! Where's Oldfield? (*Pause*) Not here, did you say? Not here? That's no excuse. Send him to me when he comes!

(*He stamps off, furiously*)

(*The scene becomes a classroom, seen from the class's angle. Boys and girls stroll in chattering and laughing. Enter* **Barrel, Pam** *and* **Allman. Barrel** *sits on the table, which is now the teacher's table:* **Pam** *stands beside him. The bed is removed*)

Allman Hey, was it you, Barrel?

Barrel (*With mock innocence*) Now would I do a thing like that?

Others Yes, you would.

Barrel Pam, I appeal to *you*.

Pam I wouldn't put it past you.

Girl Does he appeal to you, Pam?

Pam (*Embarrassed*) Mind your own business.

Girl Look at her blushing.

Pam I'm not.

Allman You could've dropped us all in it, Barrel. Thorny might've cancelled the outing.

Barrel Not him. If he'd cancelled the outing he'd have had to do some teaching. Pity Oldfield wasn't there, though.

(*Enter* **Tich**)

Allman	Talk o' the devil.
Barrel	Well, look what's crawled in. The only man as can walk under a dash-hound without knocking his hat off.
Tich	Shut your face, Barrel!
Barrel	Mr Snide to you, midget. Barrel to my friends. Where've you been anyway? We thought you were on strike, like your dad.
Tich	I missed the bus.
Allman	Briar missed you, too – in assembly. He wants to see you.
Tich	I don't care.
Barrel	(*With a sneer*) Mighty Mouse rides again.
Allman	Wheeeeeeeee! Kerpow!

(*He dive-bombs* **Tich** *and thumps him*)

Tich	Gerroff!
Barrel	You going to the zoo, Oldfield?
Tich	What of it?
Barrel	Should've stayed at home and saved yourself the bus fare. (*Laughter*)
Barrel	Are you getting it from school fund again?
Tich	No, I'm not.
Allman	Chivers calls it (*He does a bad imitation of* **Chivers**'s *voice*) 'living orff the parish'.
Boy	That don't sound like Jammy. Tich is best at imitating.
Barrel	So are monkeys. Come on, then, Oldfield. Let's see you do Chivers.
Tich	I don't feel like it.
Pam	Go on, Tich. It'll be a giggle.
Barrel	Tell you what. You all sit in your desks and Oldfield can sit in Chivers's seat just to set the scene, like.

(*Encouragement from all round. After a moment's hesitation* **Tich** *takes the teacher's chair. Someone lends him a pair of spectacles and then the rest take their seats*)

I'll go and make sure he's not coming.

(*He goes to the door, looks out, gives a momentary start then calls blandly*)

Barrel	There's nobody in sight. Get on with it.

(**Barrel** *moves hurriedly to his seat.* **Tich** *launches into a life-like imitation of* **Chivers**)

Tich   (*As* **Chivers**) Today, I want to talk to you about the causes of the disturbances in the early nineteenth century. For about six hours.

(**Chivers** *himself enters. He stops and watches with mounting annoyance, but* **Tich** *fails to notice*)

Get out your pens and write down every word I say. I don't want anybody asking any questions and if anybody interrupts me he can out and stay in. I don't want to see a single stupid face. All I'm interested in is the top of your heads.

(*On cue,* **Chivers** *clouts* **Tich** *on the top of his head with a book*)

Tich   Give over! (*Sees* **Chivers**) Oh, blimey!

Chivers   Get out of my chair, you cheeky little oaf. I suppose you think that's clever, making fun of a member of the staff.

Tich   No, sir.

Chivers   You're not fit to be in a decent school. We had civilized traditions before people like you came and brought us all down to your level. You can write me a hundred lines: 'I must not behave like an ill-bred guttersnipe.' Go and sit down and get out your book.

(**Tich** *scuttles to his seat*)

Sit up straight, the lot of you. Snide, what were we talking about last time?

Barrel   Sir, about how the workmen used to break up machines, sir.

Chivers   Correct. At least somebody's awake. The machines could do the work of several men so the workmen broke them up. Typical, of course, of the attitudes of the working class towards progress. Take your pens and write as I dictate. And I don't want anybody falling asleep. Do you hear that, Oldfield?

Tich   Yes, Sir.

Chivers   Get ready, then. 'The introduction of new machinery and the consequent increase in unemployment gave rise to wide-spread unrest. Unlawful gatherings took place at which the workmen aired their grievances and formulated plans of action . . .'

(*Everybody 'freezes' for a moment. This is the signal that* **Tich** *has gone into a daze. Like a zombie,* **Chivers** *moves away to be joined by a number of the class.* **Tich** *rises and stands on the table*)

Tich   (*Addressing the remainder*) Brothers, we've got to do something about it. (*Murmurs of agreement from the audience*) Our wives and kids are starving, while the bosses are stuffing themselves with chicken and chips. My dad says we should talk to them, but they just don't want to listen. I'm sick of being pushed around and clouted. It's time we taught 'em a lesson. Are you with me?

(*A roar of support*)

Let's go then, and smash up all the machinery in the factory.

Allman   But Davey, Mr Chivers has got the soldiers in. Look!

(*He points and they all look*)

Tich   Do you see that, men? It's war!

(*An anxious murmur passes through the crowd*)

Barrel   Davey, hadn't we better try talking, like your dad says?

Tich   What's the matter, Tub Guts? Are you scared?

Barrel   I've got a wife and family to think of, like you said.

Tich   And so have I, if it comes to that. (*Calls*) Pam!

Pam   (*In the crowd*) Yes, love?

Tich   What do you think I should do?

Pam   I'm right behind you, David, whatever you decide.

Tich   That's my Pam! You're a better man than any of them, even if you are a woman. Are any of you heroes coming with me, then?

(*Silence from the crowd*)

Right, I'll go by myself. (*Calling*) Chivers! Oy, Chivers! Show thy face.

(**Chivers** *appears at the door of his mill, with a line of soldiers in front of him*)

Chivers   Who's making all this noise? Oldfield? Is it you again? You always were a troublemaker.

Tich   I'm coming to smash those machines up, Chivers.

Chivers   You take one step in this direction, you ill-bred guttersnipe, and I'll order the soldiers to fire.

(*The soldiers bring their muskets to their shoulders*)

Barrel   He means what he says, Davey. Let's get out of here.

Tich   Shut your trap, Mighty Mouse. A man's got to do what a man's got to do.

(*He jumps off the table, seizes an axe from a member of the crowd*)

Right, Chivers, let's see what you're made of.

(*He starts to walk towards the soldiers*)

Chivers   You've asked for it, Oldfield. Fire!

(*Nothing happens*)

Chivers   (*Panic-stricken*) I said fire, didn't you hear me? Fire, damn you!

(**Tich** *halts with muskets against his chest*)

Tich   (*Calmly*) Well, comrades, are you going to fire?

(*Pause. Then the soldiers lower their muskets. The crowd cheer as the soldiers mingle with them, shaking their hands*)

Tich   (*Shouting above the noise*) Get Chivers!

(*Some of the crowd grab* **Chivers** *and bring him to* **Tich**)

Tich   Well, Mr Jammy Chivers. The boot's on the other foot, now, isn't it? What shall we do with him, mates?

Crowd   Hang him! Hang him!

Tich   Did you hear that, Chivers? The workers have decided to hang you from this here tree. (*He indicates the imaginary tree under which they are standing*) For crimes against our class. Have you anything to say?

(**Chivers** *drops on his knees*)

Chivers   Have mercy on me, for God's sake. I'm too old to die.

Tich   Get to your feet, you silly twit.

Chivers   (*Rising*) I'll cancel that imposition!

Tich   You should have thought about that before. It's too late now. Right, lads, let's proceed with the execution.

(*He mimes slipping a noose round* **Chivers'** *neck and throwing the rope over a tree-branch above. All the children return to their seats and start to drum on their desk lids. The drumming gets louder and faster, reaches a climax and ceases abruptly. There is silence and stillness for a moment. Then* **Chivers** *returns to 'life' and turns on* **Tich**)

Chivers   Oldfield, how much longer are you going to keep me hanging around? I'm waiting for an answer.

Tich   What did you say?

Chivers   Get to your feet, you insolent lout. Bring me your notebook. (*He scans it briefly*) Two sentences. Two miserable sentences. (*He beats time to this on* **Tich's** *head*) You've been dreaming again, all the time I've been talking. Well, you can just borrow somebody else's book and copy out the notes from that. And you can bring them to me in the morning, along with that imposition. Is that clear?

Tich   Yes, sir.

Chivers   Go back to your place; you make me sick. The rest of you, put your books away. There'll be no homework tonight because of this ridiculous outing. It's not my idea, I assure you! I don't know what the school is coming to.

(*He sweeps out. The class give a muffled cheer*)

(*Enter* **Miss Feckless,** *youngish, overdressed and anxious. Her authority is negligible. She carries a list of names and when she appears the children rise, carrying their chairs, and file past her as though getting onto a bus. They place their chairs in twos so that the final effect is of a cross section through it. There also enters the* **Driver,** *who picks up the table and places it at the front of the vehicle as the engine, taking one of the chairs there for himself. At the end of the queue are* **Barrel, Pam** *and* **Tich.**)

Miss F.   Darrel Snide, Pamela Russell and David Oldfield.

(**Barrel** *sits by the window,* **Pam** *next to him*)

Miss F.   What's that book you've got, David?

Tich   James Bond, Miss.

Miss F.   Oh, dear. I don't think you should be reading that. The Headmaster wouldn't approve. Keep it in your pocket, there's a good boy.

(**Tich** *shrugs and takes a solitary seat behind* **Barrel** *and* **Pam**)

Miss F.   Are we all here, then?

Class   (*In a rude sing-song*) Yes, Miss Feckless.

Miss F.   We're all here, driver. Hadn't we better get started?

Driver   (*With a leer*) Whenever you're ready, darling.

Class   Ooooooooooh! (*Kissing noises*)

(*The engine starts and the children cheer. By their movements they show that the vehicle is gathering speed.* **Tich** *takes out his book and starts to read*)

Barrel   Can we sing, Miss?

Miss F.   (*Half rising*) Oh, if you must. But please keep it quiet. And please keep it respectable. (*Sits again*)

Barrel   (*Loudly*)
Oh, dear, what can the matter be,
Fanny Feckless locked in a lavatory,

(*The rest join in*)

> She was there from Monday to Saturday,
> Nobody knew she was there.

(**Miss Feckless** *rises with a fierce look on her face and an air of uncharacteristic authority. In her hand is a pistol*)

Miss F.   Silence!

(*Silence falls*)

> Now listen to me for a change. Sit still and shut up. Allman, I'm talking to you.

Allman   (*In meek amazement*) Yes, Miss.

Miss F.   The Captain and I have something to say to you.

(*The* **Driver** *comes out of the 'cockpit'*)

Miss F.   We have taken the places of the real pilot and the air hostess. Our mission is to kidnap one of the passengers. She thinks we don't know who she is, but we have seen through her disguise. Captain.

(*The* **Driver** *seizes* **Pam** *and drags her to the front of the bus. Expressions of surprise from the rest*)

> Quiet! (*To* **Pam**) You are coming with us, my dear.

(*The* **Driver** *mimes putting a parachute onto her*)

> This is the Princess Pamelana. Her father is the King of Cleethorpes and will pay a handsome ransom. I'm afraid we'll have to leave you now. We're flying over our secret hideout. Goodbye, you little horrors. Enjoy your trip to the next world. Open the door, Captain.

(*The* **Driver** *does this. He and* **Miss Feckless** *grab* **Pam** *by the wrists*)

Pam   (*Screaming*) Help me, Darrel! Help!

Barrel   I can't do nothing, Pam.

Tich   But I can, Olga, can't I?

Miss F.   Great heavens, it's Tich Bond!

Tich   Let them go, you rotten twits. The game's up.

Miss F.   Jump, Captain, quickly!

Miss F./Driver   One, two, three . . .

(**Tich** *races forward and grabs* **Pam** *as the villains jump and float away shaking their fists. Someone closes the door*)

Pam   You saved me, Tich. You're wonderful.

Barrel What about this plane, then, Mr Wonderful? We ain't got a pilot.

Tich You'll have to make do with me, then, won't you?

Boy But you've never flown a plane, Tich, have you?

Tich I've ridden a trolley. It can't be much different. Go back to your seats, the lot of you, and fasten yourselves in. You can look after Pam for me, Snide.

(*The rest take their seats as* **Tich** *takes the controls*)

Tich Going down – now!

(*All lean forward as the plane descends. Suddenly, they lurch to the right*)

Boy Wing's fallen off!

(*They lurch the other way*)

Girl Now the other one's gone.

Tich Th'undercarriage's jammed as well. Stand by for a belly flop.

(*As the plane hits the ground, the passengers bounce up and down in their seats, and finally come to rest*)

Pam He's done it! I knew he would.

(*All babble excitedly.* **Tich** *emerges from the cockpit and holds up his hands for attention*)

Tich I know how you feel, but it's all part of the day's work. Get outside right away before the thing blows up.

(*The passengers file out past him. As they do so,* **Miss Feckless** *and the* **Driver** *reappear and stand outside the door*)

Miss F. Come on, David. You're always the last, aren't you? You are a dream. Now don't forget, boys and girls, I want you back by half-past five and please don't be late, and please be careful with the animals. Have you all got your lunch packs?

Class Yes, Miss Feckless.

Miss F. Good. We'll see you later, then, driver.

Driver Right you are, darling.

(*He removes the table. The children dismantle the bus, placing three or four chairs down the front to represent a bench seat.* **Miss Feckless** *wanders off and the party disperses*)

(*The stage remains empty for a few seconds and the air is filled with jungle noises. Then on comes* **Tich,** *hacking his way through undergrowth and creepers. He stops and wipes his brow. Then he throws back his head, beats his chest and gives a*

Tarzan call. An imaginary **Ape,** *invisible to everybody (including the audience), except* **Tich,** *lands at his feet. In the background the* **Keeper** *enters and watches, seeing only* **Tich**)

> **Tich**   (*To the imaginary ape*) Me – Tarzan; you – brother.

(**Tich** *mimes hugging the* **Ape,** *and they do a dance together. The* **Keeper** *watches* **Tich** *apparently dancing by himself. Suddenly* **Tich** *spots him and stops in embarrassment*)

> **Keeper**   They'll be putting you away, Shorthouse.
>
> **Tich**   I didn't know you were there.
>
> **Keeper**   I could see that. Who d'you think you are, then? Tarzan? More like Shaun the Leprechaun.
>
> **Tich**   I was only pretending.
>
> **Keeper**   You want some horse muck in your shoes, make you grow a bit. Are you with this school party?
>
> **Tich**   Yeh.
>
> **Keeper**   I hate kids. Feeding crocodiles wi' bubbly gum and drawing pictures on the rhinos. It's not funny, I tell you. Don't know how to treat animals, kids don't.
>
> **Tich**   No use looking at me. I never touched 'em.
>
> **Keeper**   You're all as bad. What have you come for, anyway?
>
> **Tich**   We've got to write about 'em. Poems and that.
>
> **Keeper**   Poems? What a waste of time. You want to do a day's work for a change. I was earning me living at your age.
>
> **Tich**   It's not my fault.
>
> **Keeper**   You get things too easy these days. I deserve my money, every miserable penny of it. I've got to clean monkeys out now. Like a job, would you?
>
> **Tich**   I wouldn't mind.
>
> **Keeper**   Get on with your poetry, Shakespeare. And make sure it's paper you write on.

(*He exits.* **Tich** *takes out a notebook and pencil and sits on the bench*)

> **Tich**   (*To himself*)
>   A monkey is an animal
>   That swings from bough to bough . . .

(*His mouth silently runs through the alphabet to find a rhyme, cow, dow, fow, gow etc. Enter* **Barrel** *and* **Pam** *carrying packed lunches*)

> **Barrel**   Now here's an interesting specimen, Pamela. If it had a brain it'd be almost human. (*He holds out his hand to* **Tich**) Puss, puss, puss!

Tich Get lost, Barrel.

Barrel Did you hear that, Pamela? Obviously dangerous. You sit here and I'll protect you.

(*They sit on the seat,* **Barrel** *next to* **Tich**. **Barrel** *puts his packed lunch on the seat next to* **Tich** *and opens it.* **Pam** *opens hers on her lap.* **Tich** *tries not to look.* **Barrel** *takes out a sandwich*)

Barrel What's first on the menu, then? Cheese butties. What have you got, Pam?

Pam Pork.

Barrel Hear that, Oldfield? She's eating one of your relatives.

Pam Haven't you got any sandwiches, Tich?

Tich Didn't bring any.

Pam Would you like one of mine?

Barrel You mustn't feed the animals. It's against the regulations.

Tich I'm not bothered.

Barrel There you are, you see. Oldfield's not bothered. He doesn't want a delicious cheese sandwich, flavoured with pickles, do you, Oldfield?

(*He takes a huge bite*)

Mmmmmmmmmm! Smashing! Bit of tomato to go with it.

(*He eats a tomato.* **Tich** *is suffering intensely. Unnoticed, an* **Ape** *appears in the background.* **Barrel** *finishes his sandwich. He turns to* **Pam**)

Barrel Like a drop of fizz, Pam?

Pam Oh, yes, please.

Barrel Hold your cup out, then.

(*While he pours the lemonade, the* **Ape** *steals a banana from his lunch pack and starts to eat it.* **Barrel** *takes a swig from his bottle and turns again to his lunch pack*)

Barrel Hey! Have you been at my picnic?

Tich What do you mean?

Barrel There was a banana there a minute ago.

Tich I haven't had it.

(**Barrel** *seizes him by the shirt front*)

I want that banana back, Oldfield.

(**Tich** *struggles to his feet and tries to pull away.* **Barrel** *also rises*)

Tich   I haven't got your rotten banana.

Barrel   If you've eaten it, you thieving little swine . . .

(*The* **Ape** *grabs* **Pam** *by the shoulders. She screams.* **Barrel** *turns, jumps and lets go of* **Tich**)

Pam   Get it off! Get it off!

(*The* **Ape** *pulls* **Pam** *off the seat and embraces her. The sandwiches slip to the ground.* **Pam** *squeals, hysterically*)

Barrel   Let go! Good dog! Let go – please.

(*The* **Ape** *growls at him*)

Barrel   I'm off (*He flees*)

(**Tich** *watches with a dazed look as though he is not sure whether he is dreaming or not. Then suddenly he starts to beat his chest like Tarzan. The* **Ape** *turns and looks at him quizzically*)

Tich   Me – Tarzan! You – brother!

(*The* **Ape** *bares his teeth.* **Tich** *stiffens with fright*)

Tich   Fizzin' 'ell! It doesn't work!

(*He turns and runs away. The* **Ape** *pursues him round the stage. Finally* **Tich** *falls over and the* **Ape** *places a foot on him and starts to beat his chest.* **Pam** *hops about while shouting for help. On comes the* **Keeper.** *He crosses to the* **Ape,** *takes him by the hand and pulls him away*)

Keeper   Come on, Bimbo, come with Uncle Philip. There's a good boy. He's quite harmless when he knows you. He likes a bit of fun, that's all. Are you all right, Shorthouse?

Tich   He's torn me shirt.

Keeper   That's nothing.

Tich   Nothing? My mum'll kill me. Then she'll come here and play hell.

Keeper   Look, Shorthouse, couldn't you tell her you tore it on a fence or something? I mean, she doesn't have to know it was an ape, does she? Cause a lot of trouble if anybody found out he escaped. I could swear blind I locked that cage, I really could. Not like me at all. Here, take this lot and keep your mouth shut, OK?

(*He gives* **Tich** *a handful of loose change*)

Tich   Gosh, thanks.

Keeper   Think on, Shorthouse. Let's go home, Bimbo. Uncle Philip take him home? Come on, lovie.

(*He leads the* **Ape** *away*)

Tich (*To* **Pam**) One pound and forty-five pence.

Pam Serves him right. Shove it in your pocket before he changes his mind.

Tich Are you all right?

Pam I can't stop shivering.

Tich Better sit down a minute.

(*They sit on the seat*)

Your sandwiches are all mucky.

Pam I don't want 'em anyway.

(*Pause*)

Tich I could afford a proper meal. Two meals. In t'café.

Pam I couldn't eat a thing, honest.

(*Enter* **Barrel**)

Barrel I went to get help. Somebody had to do something didn't they? You OK Pam?

Pam Bit shook up, but I'm not hurt.

Barrel Like a coffee? Best thing for nerves.

Pam Wouldn't mind.

Barrel Come on, then. There's a machine over there.

Pam What about Tich?

Barrel Oldfield can look after the stuff for us. Tell you what, Oldfield, you can have all the sandwiches that fell on the ground.

(*He puts his arm suavely and protectively round* **Pam** *and leads her away.* **Tich** *watches them go. Then he takes the money out of his pocket, looks at it, clenches it furiously in his fist and rams it decisively back into his pocket. Then he shouts*)

You stinking, fat, big-headed Sex Maniac!

(*He picks up* **Barrel***'s sandwiches, grins fiendishly and shakes them out all over the ground. Then he exits jauntily*)

(*Enter* **Tich***'s* **Mother** *with a dustpan and brush. She hums happily to herself, even, amazingly, when she cleans up the sandwiches.* **Dad** *brings on the table, dismantles the 'bench' and goes upstairs. When she has finished,* **Mother** *sits on a chair, and looks at a woman's magazine.* **Tich** *enters fearfully and stands by the door*)

Mother (*Purely for information*) Where've you been?

Tich I had to stay in, and then I missed the bus.

Mother (*With mock severity*) Eeh, you naughty lad. What are we going to do with you? Have you had any tea?

Tich No, mum.

Mother (*Bounding up*) Well what would you like, then? We've not much in, but you're welcome to what there is. Like a nice boiled egg?

Tich (*Shrinking away*) You feeling all right, mum?

Mother Right as rain. Why shouldn't I be?

Tich Where's dad?

Mother He's upstairs.

Tich Is *he* all right?

Mother Course he's all right. What's the matter with you?

(*Enter* **Father**)

Father Hello, Davey, lad. You all right, then?

Mother Don't you start.

Tich I'm all right, dad. It's mum. She's all different.

Father That's not surprising, is it, lad?

Tich What do you mean?

Father Didn't you tell him, Elsie?

Mother I haven't had a chance.

Father Strike's over, Davey. We've got a rise, a big 'un, too.

Tich A rise? That's great! Did you hang the boss?

Father (*Laughing*) We negotiated a settlement. If I had any ready money, we'd celebrate.

Tich I've got some money, dad. A quid.

Mother A quid? Where did you get that from?

Tich Found it.

Father Been a good day all round, hasn't it? What shall we spend it on, then, Davey?

Tich Let's get some chicken and chips.

Father Chicken and chips! I could just go a dollop of that. Nip out and get it, Davey.

Tich I got a better idea. Let's go and have it in the café. I've always wanted to eat in there. Save mum washing up.

Mother   (*To* **Father**) Pity *you* didn't think of that. I'll go and get my coat. David's right, we'll eat in style for once.

(*She exits*)

Tich   Wish I could find a quid every day.

Father   That only happens in dreams, lad. Best to settle for what you've got. Be back to normal tomorrow.

Mother   (*Calling from offstage, with a hint of impatience*) Are you coming, then?

Father   Before tomorrow if we don't look sharp. Lead the way, Rockefeller. Mustn't keep her waiting.

(*They go out*)

Ernie's Incredible Illucinations

CHARACTERS

Ernie — *Russell*
Mum — *Sharon Hayley*
Dad — *Matthew Copsey or Danny*
Receptionist — *Rebecca*
Doctor *Bradley.*
Officer *Matthew Green Adrian*
Auntie May — *Lee Sharon*
1st Barker —
2nd Barker —
3rd Barker —
4th Barker —
Referee — *Mich*

Timekeeper
Man — *Mark,*
Woman
Kid Saracen
2nd Man
Lady
Attendant
Tramp
Girl Librarian
Lady Librarian
Patients, Soldiers, Crowds,
Boxers, etc.

*Scene: At one side of the stage – a doctor's waiting room. It is filled with an assort-
ment of miserable-looking patients, coughing, wheezing, sneezing and moaning.
Amongst them sit* **Mr** *and* **Mrs Fraser** *and their son* **Ernie.**

Ernie	(*to audience, after a second*) If you ever want to feel ill – just go and spend a happy half-hour in a doctor's waiting room. If you're not ill when you get there, you will be when you leave.

(*A man enters, having seen the doctor. He is moaning. He crosses the waiting room
and goes out. The other patients look at him and sorrowfully shake their heads.
The* **Receptionist** *enters*)

Receptionist	Mr and Mrs Fraser . . . (**Mum** *and* **Dad** *rise*) Doctor will see you now.
Mum	Thank you. Come on, Ernie.

(**Mum** *and* **Dad** *and* **Ernie** *follow the* **Receptionist** *across the stage to the*
Doctor *who sits behind a table*)

Mum	'Morning, Doctor.

(**Receptionist** *leaves*)

Doctor	Ah. Ah. Mr and Mrs Fraser. Is that it?
Mum	That's right. I'm Mrs Fraser . . . and this is my husband, Mr Fraser . . . and this is our son . . . Ernie.
Doctor	Ah yes. Ernie. I've been hearing all sorts of things about you, young Ernie. Now, what have you been up to, eh?
Dad	Illucinations.
Doctor	I beg your pardon?
Dad	Illucinations.
Doctor	Oh, yes illuci – quite, yes.
Mum	What my husband means doctor is that Ernie has been creating these illusions.
Doctor	Ah.
Mum	Well, they're more than illusions, really.
Dad	I'll say.
Doctor	Beg pardon?
Dad	I'll say.

Mum   He's been causing that much trouble. At school, at home, everywhere he goes. I mean we can't go on like this. His Dad's not as strong as he was, are you, Albert?

Dad   No.

Doctor   What?

Dad   No.

Doctor   Perhaps it would be better if you told me a little more about it. When did you first notice this . . . ?

Mum   Ah well . . .

Dad   Ah.

Mum   Now then . . .

Dad   Now . . .

Mum   He'd have been . . . well, it'd have been about . . . near enough . . . er . . .

Doctor   Go on.

(**Ernie** *steps forward. During his speech* **Mum** *and* **Dad** *remain seated. The* **Doctor** *moves to the side of the stage, produces a notebook and makes notes on what follows*)

Ernie   It started with these daydreams. You know, the sort everybody gets. Where you suddenly score a hat trick in the last five minutes of the Cup Final or you bowl out the West Indies for ten runs . . . or saving your granny from a blazing helicopter, all that sort of rubbish.

It was one wet Saturday afternoon and me and my Mum and my Dad were all sitting about in the happy home having one of those exciting afternoon rave-ups we usually have in our house.

(**Ernie** *sits at the table in the* **Doctor**'s *chair and starts to read a book.* **Mum** *has started knitting and* **Dad** *just sits, gazing ahead of him. A long silence*)

Ernie   It was all go in our house.

(*Pause*)

Mum   I thought you'd be at the match today, Albert.

Dad   Not today.

Mum   Not often you miss a game.

Dad   They're playing away.

Mum   Oh.

Dad   In Birmingham. I'm damned if I'm going to Birmingham. Even for United.

Ernie   Meanwhile . . . while this exciting discussion was in progress, I was reading this book about the French wartime resistance workers and of the dangers they faced . . . often arrested in their homes. I started wondering what would happen if a squad of soldiers turned up at our front door, having been tipped off about the secret radio transmitter hidden in our cistern . . . when suddenly . . .

(The tramp of feet and a squad of soldiers comes marching on and up to their front door)

Officer   'Halte!' *(He bangs on the door)*

(Pause)

Dad   That the door?

Mum   What?

Dad   The door.

Mum   Was it?

Officer   Open zis door. Open the door! *(He knocks again)*

Mum   Oh, that'll be the milkman wanting his money. He always comes round about now. Albert, have you got ten bob . . . ?

Dad   *(fumbling in his pockets)* Ah . . .

Officer   *(shouting)* Open zis door immediately. Or I shall order my men to break it down. *(He bangs on the door again)*

Mum   Just a minute. Coming.

Dad   Should have one somewhere . . .

Officer   We know you're in there, English spy! Come out with your hands up . . .

Mum   What's he shouting about? Oh, I'd better ask him for three pints next week, if Auntie May's coming . . .

Officer   Zis is your last chance . . . *(He knocks again)*

Mum   Oh shut up . . .

*(The **Officer** signals his men. Two of them step back, brace their shoulders and prepare to charge the door)*

Mum   I'm coming . . . I'm coming.

Ernie   I shouldn't go out there, Mum . . .

Mum   What?

Ernie   I said don't go out there . . .

Mum   What –

Ernie   It's not the milkman. It's a squad of enemy soldiers . . .

Mum   Who?

Ernie   They've come for me . . .

Mum   Who has?

Ernie   The soldiers. They've found out about the radio transmitter . . .

Mum   What radio?

Dad   Hey, here, that's a point. Have you paid our telly licence yet, Ethel? It might be the detector van.

Mum   Oh, sit down, Albert. Stop worrying. It's just Ernie. Shut up, Ernie.

Ernie   But Mum . . .

Dad   I think I'll take the telly upstairs. Just in case . . .

(*The soldiers charge at the door. A loud crash*)

Ernie   Don't go out, Mum.

Mum   Shut up.

Dad   (*struggling with the set*) Just take it upstairs.

Ernie   Don't go.

Mum   I can't leave him out there. The way he's going he'll have the door off its hinges in a minute . . . (*She moves to the door*)

Dad   Mind your backs. Out of my way . . .

Ernie   Mum . . .

(**Mum** *opens the door just as the two soldiers are charging for the second time. They shoot past her, straight into the hall, collide with* **Dad** *and land in a heap with him.* **Dad** *manages to hold the TV set above his head and save it from breaking*)

Mum   Hey . . .

Dad   Oy!

(*The* **Officer** *and the other soldiers enter.* **Ernie** *crouches behind the table*)

Officer   Ah-ha! The house is surrounded.

Mum   Who are you?

Officer   Put up your hands. My men will search the house.

Dad   (*feebly*) Hey . . .

Officer   (*shouting up the stairs*) We know you're hiding in here, you can't get away . . .

Dad   Hey . . . *hey* . . . HEY!

Officer   Ah-ha. What have we here?

Dad   Oh. It's the telly. The neighbour's telly. Not mine.

Officer   Ah-ha.

Dad   Just fixing it for him, you see . . .

Officer   Outside.

Dad   Eh?

Officer   You will come with me.

Dad   What, in this?. I'm not going out in this rain.

Officer   Outside or I shoot.

Dad   Here . . .

Mum   Albert . . .

Ernie   Hold it. Drop those guns.

Officer   Ah, so . . . (*he raises his gun*)

Ernie   Da-da-da-da-da-da-da-da-da-da-da.

(*The soldiers collapse and are strewn all over the hall.* **Mum** *screams. Then a silence*)

Mum   Oh, Ernie. What have you done?

Ernie   Sorry, Mum.

Dad   Oh, lad . . .

Mum   Are they – dead?   unconscious

Dad   Yes.

(**Mum** *screams again*)

Dad   Steady, steady. This needs thinking about.

Mum   What about the neighbours?

Dad   Could create a bit of gossip, this could.

Mum   What about the carpet? Look at it.

Dad   Hasn't done that much good.

Mum   What'll we do with them?

Dad   Needs a bit of thinking about.

(**Ernie** *steps forward. As he speaks during the next section,* **Dad** *and* **Mum** *carry off the bodies*)

Ernie   Well, Mum and Dad decided that the best thing to do was to pretend it hadn't happened. That was usually the way they coped with all emergencies . . .

(**Doctor** *steps forward*)

Mum	(*struggling with a body*) We waited till it got dark, you see . . .
Doctor	Yes? And then . . . ?
Dad	We dumped 'em.
Doctor	I beg your pardon?
Dad	We dumped 'em. Took 'em out and dumped 'em.
Doctor	Dumped them? Where, for heaven's sake?
Dad	Oh . . . bus shelters . . . park benches . . .
Mum	Corporation car park.
Dad	Left one in the all-night cafeteria.
Mum	And one in the Garden of Rest.
Dad	Caused a bit of a rumpus.
Doctor	I'm not surprised.
Mum	We had the police round our way for days – trying to sort it out . . .
Dad	They never did get to the bottom of it, though.
Doctor	Extraordinary. And then?
Ernie	(*stepping forward*) And then – Auntie May arrived to stay. I liked my Auntie May.

(**Auntie May** *enters.* **Doctor** *steps back again*)

Auntie	'Ullo, Ernie lad. Have a sweetie.
Ernie	Ta, Auntie. And Auntie May took me to the fair.

(*The stage is filled with jostling people, barkers and fairground music*)

1st Barker	Yes, indeed, the world's tallest man! He's so tall, madam, his breakfast is still sliding down him at tea time. Come along now, sir. Come inside now . . .
2nd Barker	(*simultaneously*) Ladies and Gentlemen. I am prepared to guarantee that you will never again, during your lifetimes, see anything as unbelievably amazing as the Incredible Porcupine Woman. See her quills and get your thrills. Direct from the unexplored South American Jungle . . .
3rd Barker	Try your luck . . . come along, Madam . . . leave your husband there, dear, he'll still be there when you come back . . . tell you what – if he isn't I can sell you a replacement . . . five shots for sixpence . . . knock 'em all down and pick up what you like . . .

Ernie	Can I have a go on that, Auntie?
Auntie	Not now, Ernie.
Ernie	Oh go on, Auntie May.
Auntie	I want a cup of tea.
Ernie	Have an ice-cream.
Auntie	I've had three. I can't have any more. It'll bring on my condition . . .
Ernie	What condition, Auntie?
Auntie	Never you mind what. But I should never have had that candy floss as well. I'll suffer for it.
4th Barker	Just about to start, Ladies and Gentlemen. A heavyweight boxing bout, featuring the one and only unofficial challenger for the heavyweight champion of the world – Kid Saracen. The Kid will be fighting this afternoon, for the very first time, a demonstration contest against the new sensation from Tyneside, Eddie 'Grinder' Edwards. In addition, Ladies and Gentlemen, the Kid is offering fifty pounds – yes, fifty pounds – to any challenger who manages to last three three-minute rounds . . .
Ernie	Oh, come on Auntie. Let's go in and watch.
Auntie	What is it?
Ernie	Boxing.
Auntie	Boxing? I'm not watching any boxing. I don't mind wrestling but I'm not watching boxing. It's bloodthirsty.
Ernie	Auntie . . .
Auntie	Nasty stuff, boxing . . .
4th Barker	Come along, lady. Bring in the young gentleman. Let him see the action . . .
Auntie	Oh no . . .
4th Barker	Come along. Two is it?
Ernie	Yes please. Two.
4th Barker	Thank you, son.
Auntie	Eh?
Ernie	This way, Auntie.

(*Before* **Auntie May** *can protest, she and* **Ernie** *are inside the boxing booth. The crowd have formed a square around the ring in which stand* **Kid Saracen, Eddie Edwards** *and the* **Referee**)

Ref   Ladies and Gentlemen, introducing on my right, the ex-unofficial challenger for the World Heavyweight Champion-ship – Kid Saracen . . .

(Boos from the crowd)

And on my left the challenger from Newcastle upon Tyne . . . Eddie Edwards . . .

(Crowd cheers)

(To boxers) Right, I want a good clean fight, lads. No low blows and when I say break, stop boxing right away. Good luck.

Timekeeper   Seconds out –

(The bell rings. The crowd cheers as the boxers size each other up. They mostly cheer on **Edwards** *– 'Come on, Eddie' 'Murder him, Eddie', etc. Boxers swap a few punches)*

Auntie   Oooh. I can't look.

(The man next to her starts cheering)

Man   Flatten him, Eddie.

*(***Auntie** *peers out from behind her hands in time to see the* **Kid** *clout* **Eddie** *fairly hard)*

Auntie   Hey, you stop that.

Man   Get at him, Eddie . . .

Auntie   Yes, that's right, get at him.

Man   Hit him.

Auntie   Knock him down.

Man   Smash him.

Auntie   Batter him. *(She starts to wave her arms about in support of* **Eddie,** *throwing punches at the air)*

Man   That's it, missis. You show 'em.

Auntie   I would, I would.

Man   Give 'em a run for their money, would you?

Auntie   I'm not that old . . .

Man   Eddie!

Auntie   Come on, Eddie!

Ernie   Eddie!

(In the ring **Kid** *throws a terrific blow which brings* **Eddie** *to his knees)*

Ref One . . . two . . . three . . .

Man Get up, Eddie . . .

Auntie Get up . . . get up . . .

Ref . . . four . . .

(**Eddie** *rises and blunders round the ring. The* **Kid** *knocks him clean out.*

The **Referee** *counts him out. Crowd boos wildly. The* **Kid** *walks smugly round the ring, his hands raised above his head in triumph*)

Auntie You brute.

Man Boo. Dirty fight . . .

Auntie Bully . . .

Ref (*quietening the crowd*) And now – Ladies and Gentlemen, the Kid wishes to issue a challenge to any person here who would like to try his skill at lasting three rounds . . . any person here. Come along now . . . anybody care to try . . .

(*Muttering from the crowd*)

Auntie (*to the* **Man**) Go on then.

Man Who, me?

Auntie What are you frightened of, then?

Man I'm frightened of him . . .

Ref Come along now. We're not asking you to do it for nothing. We're offering fifty pounds . . . fifty pounds, gentlemen . . .

Auntie Go on. Fifty quid.

Man I'd need that to pay the hospital bill . . .

Auntie Go on . . .

Man It's all right for you, lady . . . just standing there telling other people to go and get their noses broken.

Auntie All right, then. I'll go in myself. Excuse me . . . (*She starts to push through the crowd towards the ring*)

Man Hey . . .

Ernie Auntie, where are you going?

Auntie Out of my way . . .

Man Hey, stop her . . . she's off her nut . . .

Ernie Auntie!

Auntie (*hailing the* **Referee**) Hey, you . . .

Ref Hallo, lady, what can we do for you? Come to challenge him, have you?

(*Laughter from the crowd*)

Auntie That's right. Help me in.

Ref Just a minute, lady, you've come the wrong way for the jumble sale, this is a boxing ring . . .

Auntie I know what it is. Wipe that silly smile off your face. Come on then, rings out of your seconds . . .

(*Crowd cheers*)

Ref Just a minute. Just a minute. What do you think you're playing at . . . ?

Auntie You said anyone could have a go, didn't you?

Woman That's right. Give her a go, then.

Ref (*getting worried*) Now, listen . . .

Kid Saracen Go home. There's a nice old lady . . .

(*Crowd boos*)

Auntie You cheeky ha'porth.

2nd Man Hit him, Grandma.

(*Crowd shouts agreement*)

Ref Tell you what, folks. Let's give the old lady ten shillings for being a good sport . . .

Auntie I don't want your ten bob . . . Come on.

Woman Get the gloves on, Granny.

Auntie I don't need gloves. My hands have seen hard work. I was scrubbing floors before he was thought of . . .

Woman That's right, love.

Ernie (*stepping forward*) And then suddenly I got this idea. Maybe Auntie May could be the new heavyweight champion of the world . . .

(*The bell rings.* **Auntie May** *comes bouncing out of her corner flinging punches at the* **Kid** *who looks startled. Crowd cheers*)

Auntie Let's have you.

Kid Saracen Hey, come off it!

(**Ref** *tries vainly to pull* **Auntie** *back but she dances out of reach*)

Kid Saracen Somebody chuck her out.

(**Kid** *turns to appeal to the crowd.* **Auntie** *punches him in the back*)

Auntie Gotcher.

Kid Saracen Ow!

(**Auntie** *bombards the* **Kid** *with punches*)

Ernie (*commentator style*) And Auntie May moves in again and catches the Kid with a left and a right to the body and there's a right cross to the head – and that really hurt him – and it looks from here as if the champ is in real trouble . . . as this amazing sixty-eight-year-old challenger follows up with a series of sharp left jabs . . . one, two, three, four jabs . . .

(*The* **Kid** *is reeling back*)

And then, bang, a right hook and he's down . . .

(**Kid** *goes down on his knees. Crowd cheers*)

Auntie (*to* **Ref**) Go on. Start counting.

Crowd One – two – three – four – five – six . . .

(*The* **Kid** *gets up again*)

Ernie And the Kid's on his feet but he's no idea where he is . . . and there's that tremendous right uppercut . . . and he's down again . . .

(**Crowd** *counts him out.* **Auntie** *dances round the ring with glee. The crowd bursts into the ring and* **Auntie** *is lifted on to their shoulders. They go out singing 'For she's a jolly good fellow'.* **Referee** *and the* **Kid** *are left*)

Ref Come on. Get up – Champ.

Kid Saracen Ooooh. (*He staggers to his feet*)

(**Kid** *goes out supported by the* **Referee. Ernie, Dad, Mum** *and the* **Doctor** *are left*)

Doctor (*still writing, excitedly*) Absolutely incredible!

Mum Terrible it was. It took it out of her, you know. She was laid up all Sunday.

Dad And we had all those fellows round from the Amateur Boxing Association trying to sign her up to fight for the Combined Services.

Mum So I told his Dad on the Monday, seeing as it was half term, 'Take him somewhere where he won't get into trouble,' I said. 'Take him somewhere quiet.'

Dad So I took him down to the library.

(**Doctor** *retires to the side of the stage again.* **Dad, Mum** *and* **Ernie** *exit.*

The scene becomes the Public Library. It is very quiet. Various people tip-toe about. At one end sits an intellectual-looking lady with glasses, reading; at the other, an old tramp eating his sandwiches from a piece of newspaper. One or two others. A uniformed attendant walks up and down importantly.

The **Lady with glasses** *looks up at the lights. She frowns)*

Lady	Excuse me . . .
Attendant	Sssshhh!
Lady	Sorry. (*Mouthing silently*) The light's gone.
Attendant	(*mouthing*) What?
Lady	(*whispering*) I said the light's gone over here.
Attendant	(*whispering*) What?
Lady	New bulb.
Attendant	(*shakes his head, not understanding*)
Lady	(*loudly*) UP THERE! YOU NEED A NEW BULB – IT'S GONE. I CAN'T SEE.
People	Sssshhhh!
Attendant	(*whispering*) Right.
Lady	(*whispering*) Thank you.

(**Attendant** *tip-toes out as* **Dad** *and* **Ernie** *tip-toe in*)

Dad	(*to* **Ernie**) Sssshhhh!

(**Ernie** *nods. They tip-toe and sit*)

Ernie	(*to audience*) I didn't really think much of this idea of my Mum's . . .
People	Ssssshhhh!
Ernie	(*whispering*) I didn't really think much of this idea of my Mum's. It was a bit like sitting in a graveyard only not as exciting. The trouble is, in library reading rooms some bloke's pinched all the best magazines already and you're left with dynamic things like *The Pig Breeder's Monthly Gazette* and suchlike. I'd got stuck with *The Bell Ringer's Quarterly*. Which wasn't one of my hobbies. Nobody else seemed to be enjoying themselves either. Except the bloke eating his sandwiches in the corner. I reckoned he wasn't a tramp at all, but a secret agent heavily disguised, waiting to pass on some secret documents to his contact who he was to meet in the library and who was at this very moment lying dead in the Reference Section, a knife in his ribs. Realising this, the tramp decides to pick on the most trustworthy-looking party in the room . . . My Dad!

(*The* **Tramp** *gets up stealthily and moves over to* **Dad.** *As he passes him he knocks his magazine out of his hand*)

Dad   Hey!

Tramp   Beg pardon mister. (*He bends to pick up the magazine and hands it back to* **Dad.** *As he does so he thrusts his newspaper parcel into* **Dad's** *hands*)

Tramp   Sssshhhh. Take this. Quickly. They're watching me. Guard it with your life.

Dad   Eh?

(**Tramp** *hurries away. A sinister man in a mackintosh gets up and follows him out*)

Dad   Who the heck was that?

Ernie   Dunno, Dad.

Dad   (*examining the parcel*) What's all this, then?

Ernie   Dunno.

Dad   I don't want his sandwiches. Spoil my dinner. (*As he unwraps the parcel*) Hey!

Ernie   What is it?

Dad   Looks like a lot of old blue-prints and things. Funny. This anything to do with you?

Ernie   (*innocently*) No, Dad.

(**Attendant** *enters with a step-ladder. He places it under the light. A* **Girl Librarian** *who has entered with him steadies the steps.* **Attendant** *produces a bulb from his pocket and starts to climb the steps*)

Ernie   (*who has been watching him*) And now, as Captain Williams nears the summit of this, the third highest mountain in the world, never before climbed by man . . .

(*Wind noises start*)

Ernie   He pauses for a moment through sheer exhaustion . . .

(**Attendant** *feeling the effects of the wind clings to the ladder for dear life. It sways slightly*)

Attendant   (*shouting down to the librarian*) More slack. I need more slack on the rope . . .

Librarian   (*shouting up to him*) More slack . . . Are you all right?

Attendant   I – think – I can . . . make it.

Librarian   Be careful. The rock looks treacherous just above you.

Attendant   It's all right. It's – quite safe – if I . . . just aaaaaahhh! (*He slips and holds on with one hand*)

Lady   Captain! What's happened?

Attendant   Damn it. I think I've broken my leg . . .

Lady   Oh, no.

Librarian   How are we going to get him down?

(**Dad** *rises*)

Ernie   And here comes Major Fraser, ace daredevil mountaineer, to the rescue.

Dad   Give me a number three clambering iron and a hydraulic drill lever, will you? I'm going up.

Librarian   Oh no, Major.

Dad   It's the only way.

Lady   Don't be a fool, Major.

Dad   Someone's got to go. Give me plenty of line . . . (*He starts to climb*)

Librarian   Good luck.

Lady   Good luck.

(*A sequence in which* **Dad** *clambers up the ladder buffeted by the wind*)

Dad   Can you hold on?

Attendant   Not – much – longer.

Dad   Try, man, try. Not much longer . . .

Lady   Keep going, man.

(**Dad** *reaches the* **Attendant**. *People cheer. The two men slowly descend the ladder*)

Ernie   And here comes the gallant Major Fraser, bringing the injured Captain Williams to safety . . .

(**Dad** *and* **Attendant** *reach the floor. More cheers and applause from the onlookers. The* **Attendant** *is still supported by* **Dad** *with one arm round his neck. General shaking of hands. Wind noise stops*)

Attendant   (*coming back to reality, suddenly*) Hey, hey! What's going on here? (*To* **Dad**) What do you think you're doing?

Dad   Oh.

Attendant   Let go of me.

Dad   Sorry I–

Attendant   Never known anything like it. This is a public building you know . . .

Dad   Ernie . . .

Ernie   Yes, Dad.

Dad   Did you start this?

Ernie   (*innocent*) Me, Dad?

Dad   Now listen, lad–

(*A second* **Librarian** *enters screaming*)

2nd Librarian   Oh, Mr Oats, Mr Oats . . .

Attendant   What's the matter, girl? What's the matter?

2nd Librarian   There's a man in the Reference Section.

Attendant   Well?

2nd Librarian   He's dead.

Lady   Dead?

2nd Librarian   Yes. I think he's been killed. There's a knife sticking in his ribs . . .

(*First* **Librarian** *screams.* **Attendant** *hurries out followed by the others, leaving* **Ernie** *and* **Dad**)

Dad   Ernie!

Ernie   Sorry, Dad.

(**Doctor** *moves in.* **Mum** *joins them*)

Doctor   Incredible.

Dad   Embarrassing.

Doctor   Yes, yes.

(*The scene is now back to where it was at the beginning, with the four in the* **Doctor**'s *room on one side and the waiting room full of patients on the other*)

Mum   Can you do anything, Doctor?

Doctor   Mmmm. Not much, I'm afraid.

Mum   No?

Doctor   You see, it's not really up to me at all. It's up to you. An interesting case. Very. In my twenty years as a general practitioner I've never heard anything quite like it. You see, this is a classic example of group hallucinations . . .

Dad   Illucinations, yes.

Doctor   Starting with your son and finishing with you all being affected . . .

Mum   All?

Doctor All of you. You must understand that all this has happened only in your minds.

Dad Just a minute. Are you suggesting we're all off our onions?

Doctor Off your . . . ?

Dad You know. Round the thing. Up the whatsit.

Doctor No . . .

Dad My missis as well?

Doctor No. No.

Dad Then watch it.

Doctor I was just explaining . . .

Dad You don't need. It's Ernie here, that's all. He imagines things and they happen.

Doctor Oh, come now. I can't really accept that.

Dad Why not?

Doctor It's – impossible. He may *imagine* things–

Dad He does.

Doctor But they don't *really* happen. They *appear* to, that's all.

Dad Is that so?

Doctor Of course.

(*Slight pause*)

Dad Ernie.

Ernie Yes, Dad.

Dad Imagine something. We'll see who's nutty.

Ernie What, Dad?

Dad Anything, son, anything. Just to show the Doctor.

Mum Nothing nasty, Ernie. Something peaceful . . .

Dad How about a brass band? I like brass bands.

Mum Oh dear. Couldn't it be something quieter? Like – a mountain stream or something . . .

Dad Don't be daft, Ethel. The Doctor doesn't want a waterfall pouring through his surgery. Go on lad. A brass band.

Ernie Right, Dad. (*He concentrates*)

(*A pause*)

Mum Come on Ernie. (*Pause*) He's usually very good at it, Doctor.

Dad   Come on, lad.

Ernie   It's difficult, Dad, I can't picture them.

Doctor   Yes, well I'm afraid I can't afford any more time just now, Mr and Mrs Fraser. I do have a surgery full of people waiting to see me . . . (*Calls*) Miss Bates! . . . so you will understand I really must get on.

Receptionist   (*enters*) Yes, Doctor.

Doctor   The next patient, please, Miss Bates.

Receptionist   (*going*) Yes, Doctor.

Doctor   (*getting up and pacing up and down as he speaks*) What I suggest we do is, I'll arrange an appointment with a specialist and . . . he'll be able to give you a better diagnosis . . . (*His steps become more and more march like*) than I will. I'm quite sure – that – a – few – sessions – with a trained – psychiatrist – will – be – quite – sufficient – to – put – everything – right – right – left – right – left – left – left – right – left . . .

(*The **Doctor** marches to the door of his room, does a smart about turn and marches round his desk. He is followed by the patients from the waiting room, some limping, some marching and all playing, or as if playing, brass instruments*)

L-e-e-e-ft . . . Wheel . . .

(*After a triumphal circuit of the room everyone marches out following the **Doctor** who has assumed the rôle of drum major*)

Ernie   (*just before he leaves*) It looks as though the Doctor suffers from illucinations as well. I hope you don't get 'em. Ta-ta.

(*He marches out jauntily, following the band*)

The End

ACTIVITIES

Daydream Believer

Have you ever found yourself daydreaming?

 a) Brainstorm the word **Daydream**.

In the brainstorm show when you daydream, where and why. Try to include daydreams you have had.

The most important feature of a brainstorm is to include as many ideas as possible whilst they are fresh in your mind. The brainstorm below should help you to get started.

WHEN I'M TIRED — DAYDREAM — ON THE BUS — ABOUT WINNING A FORTUNE

b) Compare your brainstorm with those made by other members of your class and discuss any striking similarities or differences.

c) There are a number of other words which people use to describe a daydream such as 'fantasy' or 'trance'. These alternative words are called synonyms. Work with a partner to create a list of synonyms for daydream. You may find it useful to check your own list against others in the class or look up the word in a thesaurus.

'You know, the sort everybody gets. Where you suddenly score a hat-trick in the last five minutes of the Cup final or you bowl out the West Indies for ten runs …
… or saving your granny from a blazing helicopter …'

2 Use the information from the play *Ernie's Incredible Illucinations* to fill in a copy of the following daydream chart. You will need to decide for yourself what is really happening to Ernie and when he seems to be dreaming.

What is really happening to Ernie?	Ernie's daydream
He is sitting at home reading a book about the French resistance	A troop of German soldiers appear searching for a radio
Auntie May takes him to the fair.	Auntie May becomes a champion boxer.

3 Create a similar chart for Tich Oldfield.

4 Display your charts and discuss in what ways the everyday reality of Tich and Ernie's lives and the type of dreams they have are similar or dissimilar. Why do you think that Tich and Ernie both daydream so much? You may find it helpful to look at your own brainstorms as well as referring back to the plays.

Dream Diaries

Dreams can be fascinating and are often worth recording.

WEDNESDAY NOVEMBER 1ST

What a brilliant dream! There I was on "A Million to One" with that smarmy Gooey Smiles. He was all talk, as usual, but Pam was the hostess and the audience loved her.

When it came to that part of the show where all the contestants repeat a part of their acts I really laughed...

Barrel was trying to be a pop star and he looked more overweight than ever in his stupid clothes. His singing was even worse and the crowd all booed.

Jammy Chivers was next. Boring us all to death as usual. Then I gave the crowd a series of my impressions. The audience went wild, the clapometer exploded and I won the million pounds.

When Smiles presented me with the cheque mum and dad were up on stage as well. It was fantastic.

If you would like to keep your own dream diary make sure you have a note-pad close to your bed because it helps to jot down details as soon as you wake up. You can then write up the dream in your diary.

Look out for details which often occur in your dreams. There are many books written about the meaning of dreams and you may wish to research into the significance of certain dreams.

Fear and Fantasies

Many dreams reflect both our fears and fantasies. The two poems on this page have been chosen because they suggest that although our dreams can seem strange and difficult to understand they may still portray a mysterious or frightening truth.

Dreampoem

in a corner of my bedroom
grew a tree
a happytree
my own tree
its leaves were soft
like flesh
and its birds sang poems for me
then
without warning
two men
with understanding smiles
and axes
made out of forged excuses
came and chopped it down
either yesterday
or the day before
i think it was the day before

Roger McGough

A Phantasy

This plump boy, simple, scared of everything
Told me he'd like to live in a cardboard box
With eye holes, ear holes, air holes.

After two years of treatment he had reached the point
Where only one fear remained: drowning.
He had nightmares of being sucked into the waves.

A hundred miles from the sea, walking
To school along a road two miles from any water,
A grain truck passed him on a tight corner,

Spilled its load over him.
The driver said he saw the grain moving
And tried, though injured, to dig down.

There were sounds too. Long bleating cries.
He thought it was a sheep he'd buried.
And the boy died.

John Ashbrook

 Write your own 'Dreampoem' or 'A Phantasy' in which you explore the world of fears and nightmares.

You may choose to begin your poem with the words 'in this corner of the bedroom' and describe whatever lurks there. Or you may choose to write a poem which contains the words 'Where only one fear remained:' and explain the powerful nature of that fear.

Group Illucinations

Ladies and Gentlemen. I am prepared to guarantee that you will never again, during your lifetimes, see anything as unbelievably amazing as the Incredible Porcupine Woman. See her quills and get your thrills. Direct from the unexplored South American Jungle ...

Just about to start, Ladies and Gentlemen. A heavyweight boxing bout, featuring the one and only unofficial challenger for the heavyweight championship of the world – Kid Saracen. The Kid will be fighting this afternoon, for the very first time, a demonstration contest against the new sensation from Tyneside, Eddie 'Grinder' Edwards. In addition, Ladies and Gentlemen, the Kid is offering fifty pounds – yes, fifty pounds – to any challenger who manages to last three three-minute rounds ...

Try your luck ... come along, Madam ... leave your husband there, dear, he'll still be there when you come back ... tell you what – if he isn't I can sell you a replacement ... five shots for sixpence ... knock 'em all down and pick up what you like ...

1 Invent a fairground barker's cry to attract the customers to your own sideshow. Remember to make your cry as interesting as possible by providing those tempting details which will make your stall seem more exciting than the others.

2 Take turns to shout your cries around a group and then practise crying at the same time as other members of the group. You could now try shouting across and around the class in order to develop your illusion of being at the fairground.

3 What other sound effects could you add to increase the sense of being at the fair?

4 Your illusion can now be used as a background scene-setter for further group drama work or taped for use in a radio play.

5 In groups create and tape illusions of other settings where you can experiment with a variety of sounds or noises. Scenes which feature a large gathering of different types of people such as a market-place or a seaside resort are excellent choices for this type of work.

When you have taped your illusion, play it back to the rest of the class.

> *Scene: At one side of the stage – a doctor's waiting room. It is filled with an assortment of miserable-looking patients, coughing, wheezing, sneezing and moaning. Amongst them sit* **Mr** *and* **Mrs Fraser** *and their son* **Ernie.**
>
> **Ernie**　*(to audience, after a second)* If you ever want to feel ill – just go and spend a happy half-hour in a doctor's waiting room. If you're not ill when you get there, you will be when you leave.
>
> *(A man enters, having seen the doctor. He is moaning. He crosses the waiting room and goes out. The other patients look at him and sorrowfully shake their heads.*
>
> *The* **Receptionist** *enters)*
>
> **Receptionist**　Mr and Mrs Fraser … (**Mum** *and* **Dad** *rise*) Doctor will see you now.

6　Look at how Alan Ayckbourn sets the scene which introduces Ernie and his parents in the doctor's waiting room. In groups stage your own opening to the play *Ernie's Incredible Illucinations* and experiment by having different patients waiting in the queue or walking in and out of the surgery.

7　Now you have practised establishing a scene and creating an atmosphere, whilst using very few words, try to devise an alternative setting for an incredible, group illucination.

Once again you may find it helpful to think of places where a small group of people would naturally gather and introduce various characters into a chosen setting.

You could write a script for your illucination or improvise.

Once you have set up your opening take it in turns to be Ernie and lead the illucination by saying and completing the line,

'When suddenly I started wondering what would happen if . . .'

The other characters in the scene should respond to the lead they have been given and your improvisation will be under way.

'When suddenly I started wondering what would happen if these animals could talk.'

Talk Talk – Accent/Dialect

Accent means the way words are pronounced in a particular area or by a particular group of people.

 In pairs prepare a reading of the following extract featuring Jammy Chivers and Tich Oldfield. Before you begin think carefully about the attitudes of the two characters towards each other and the voices and accents you will need to use.

(**Barrel** *moves hurriedly to his seat.* **Tich** *launches into a life-like imitation of* **Chivers**)

> Tich   (*As* **Chivers**) Today, I want to talk to you about the causes of the disturbances in the early nineteenth century. For about six hours.

(**Chivers** *himself enters. He stops and watches with mounting annoyance, but* **Tich** *fails to notice*)

> Get out your pens and write down every word I say. I don't want anybody asking any questions and if anybody interrupts me he can out and stay in. I don't want to see a single stupid face. All I'm interested in is the top of your heads.

(*On cue,* **Chivers** *clouts* **Tich** *on the top of his head with a book*)

> Tich   Give over! (*Sees* **Chivers**) Oh, blimey!

> Chivers   Get out of my chair, you cheeky little oaf. I suppose you think that's clever, making fun of a member of the staff.

> Tich   No, sir.

> Chivers   You're not fit to be in a decent school. We had civilised traditions before people like you came and brought us all down to your level. You can write me a hundred lines: 'I must not behave like an ill-bred guttersnipe.' Go and sit down and get out your book.

(**Tich** *scuttles to his seat*)

> Sit up straight, the lot of you. Snide, what were we talking about last time?

> Barrel   Sir, about how the workmen used to break up machines, sir.

> Chivers   Correct. At least somebody's awake. The machines could do the work of several men so the workmen broke them up. Typical, of course, of the attitudes of the working class towards progress. Take your pens and write as I dictate. And I don't want anybody falling asleep. Do you hear that, Oldfield?

> **Tich** Yes, Sir.
> **Chivers** Get ready, then. 'The introduction of new machinery and
> the consequent increase in unemployment gave rise to
> widespread unrest. Unlawful gatherings took place at which
> the workmen aired their grievances and formulated
> plans of action ...'

2 Now discuss the following points together:

a) How would you describe the accents you used for each character?

b) Why did you choose those accents?

Dialect means words and word orders used only in a particular area or by a particular group of people.

---

3 With a partner make up a conversation in which Tich later tells a school friend about the incident where he was caught imitating Jammy Chivers.

Try your conversation out on other people in the class and ask them to listen carefully and identify words and phrases which seem special to Tich and his friend or which they would not use in a conversation with Jammy Chivers.

4 Make a completed copy of the chart below by writing down any words or phrases which seem special to the characters Dad and The Doctor in *Ernie's Incredible Illucinations*. Include examples of things which one character would say and the other never would. Also write in examples of where they express the same idea differently or misunderstand each other.

The Doctor	Dad
You see, this is a classic example of group hallucinations.	Illucinations.
You must understand that this happened only in your minds.	Are you suggesting we're all off our onions?

5 When you have completed your chart write out what Dad and the Doctor would say about the other character, the way he talks and the type of person he seems to be.

Why do you think Alan Ayckbourn chose to make Dad and the Doctor talk as they do?

6 'In the play *Ernie's Incredible Illucinations* the doctor speaks the best English.'

In groups discuss the above statement and decide if you *agree* with the point being made, *disagree* or feel *it depends*. You will be reporting back to the rest of the class so remember to note the reasons for your decision.

The Game Show Game Show

'Thank you, ladies and gentlemen, thank you. This is your host, Gooey Smiles, and you are tuned in to *The Game Show Game Show*. So read on below and show what you know . . .'

Gooey's Game One: 'Can you find 50?'

1   In groups you have exactly five minutes to write down the names of all the quiz and game shows which you can think of and see if you can find 50, starting from now.

Gooey's Game Two: 'Pick A Talk'

2   In groups pick a game show which your group would like to examine in closer detail. Each member of the group should choose one of the game show feature cards and read it closely.

The Contestants:

- How many contestants are there?
- Describe them carefully.
- How are they treated by the presenter?
- How were they picked to appear on the show?
- Why do you think these particular contestants were selected for the show?

The Set Design:

- Describe the set carefully including information about colour, lights and general layout.
- How expensive do you think the set is?
- What does the set contribute to the presentation and drama of the show?

The Presenter/s:

- Who is the main presenter?
- Describe the main presenter carefully, especially appearance, manner and style.
- How does the presenter treat the contestants?
- Why do you think that the presenter was chosen to host this show?

The Games:

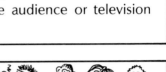

- Explain the games and their rules.
- How skilful are the games?
- How spectacular or dramatic are the games?
- Do the games encourage members of the audience or television viewers to 'play' along with a contestant?

The Audience:

- What age group/s do you think enjoy your chosen show?
- Are there any aspects of the show which would appeal to a particular age group?
- Is your show broadcast at a time which would attract a particular age group or type of person?

Prizes:

- Does the show give away many prizes?
- Are the prizes expensive?
- Are the prizes an important feature of the show?
- Do you think the prizes are the main reason that contestants appear on the show?

3 Whilst watching the chosen game show concentrate upon those questions which appear on your feature card and jot down notes ready to report back to your group.

4 Listen to each group member's information and then prepare a four minute group presentation for the rest of the class explaining why your selected show is a popular success or failure.

5 Try to organise your material so that the presentation is lively, interesting and a reflection of the group's opinion and style. There are no prizes for this game but you should have the satisfaction of receiving a good round of applause on the clapometer.

Invent a Game Show

 You have been asked to devise a new game for the television company Network Twelve.

In groups read through the following memo from the company's represent-ative, Suzie Barnes, and decide how your own game show would cover each of the eight points she mentions.

NETWORK TWELVE

MEMO

From: Suzie Barnes
To: Light Entertainments
Subject: New Game Shows
27 November 1991

I would like the proposed outline for your new game show as quickly as possible. We desperately need a thirty-minute programme which will boost our family viewing figures whilst holding production costs at an acceptable level.

You will be given the opportunity to present and discuss a pilot version of your show at a meeting to be announced. It is essential that your presentation covers all of the following aspects:

1)   The general theme of the show and the type of questions or activity games it will feature.
2)   Information about all of those people who will feature in the show such as members of the public and/or celebrities including details about the audience if you choose to have one.
3)   The style and personality of your presenter.
4)   Type of prizes.
5)   Set design and special features.
6)   The running order and organisation of the show and its various parts.
7)   Details about the atmosphere of the show and any novelty features or gimmicks which you intend to use.
8)   Suggested name or names for your show.

I look forward to hearing your proposals.

Suzie Barnes

Plan the Pilot

2 When your group has decided how the new show will deal with all of the points raised in the memo you can begin to plan your pilot presentation.

Plan the introduction and opening section of your show by drawing up a storyboard of shots and script. Look at the example storyboard of *A Million To One* which illustrates how viewers will be introduced to the show and its rules.

Note about camera shots:
C/U = a close-up   M/S = a medium distance shot   L/S = a long shot

C/U Title board	L/S Gooey on steps	C/U Gooey
Sound: Introductory music. [Voice over:] It's *A Million To One*	Sound: Introductory music. [Voice over:] And here is your host, Gooey Smiles.	Sound: [Gooey] Good evening ladies and gentlemen and welcome to *A Million to One*

M/S Gooey	M/S Pam
Sound: [Gooey] The show where you decide upon the stars of tomorrow and we hold out that million to one chance.	Sound: [Gooey] And with me as always . . . a hand please for the delightful Pam. (Audience applause)

3 Prepare the publicity materials for your show such as a programme listing for a magazine or newspaper and the television announcement made to create interest in your show before it is broadcast.

4 Now act out the opening section to your show. Aim to make your presentation brief, polished, tempting and informative.

Staging a Play

Whether you are staging one of the two plays in this book or producing your own play about dreams and illusions you will be faced with the problem of presenting a number of different scenes which change constantly between fantasy and reality. These problems can be overcome by using techniques which invite the audience to accept your play as a dramatic illusion and encourage them to enjoy the 'make believe' nature of your production.

Some effects to consider are:

- the use of 'group illucination' sound effects or tapes such as those suggested on page 42
- hand-held props or basic items of costume
- the use of simple stage props such as a table or chair for different purposes
- the use of slides or acetates on an overhead projector to establish the backdrop for a scene
- lighting changes to convey setting and create atmosphere.

You are to present your ideas for production to the management committee of The Round Theatre Group, a company which aims to stage plays which could be shown at a wide range of venues around the country including school drama studios or even classrooms.

Optional items include

- Basic sound equipment
- Projection equipment and screen
- Spotlight and blackout facility

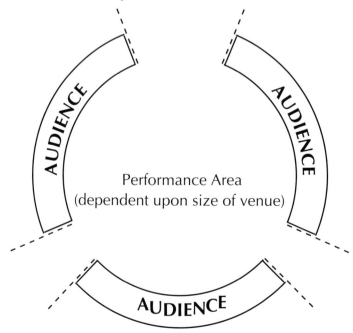

Basic plan of the Round Theatre

1 In groups you will be expected to produce and act out at least one scene which features a transformation between fantasy and reality or vice versa. You will need to persuade the committee that your production would suit The Round Theatre so divide up the tasks between your group members and prepare precise details of the following:

- the cast list
- hand-held props and essential costume items to be worn by characters
- basic stage layout including details of prop positions and clearly marked character entrances and exits
- special lighting, sound or visual effects.

Remember that The Round Theatre Group tend to look favourably upon productions which demonstrate **imagination, organisation** and **simplicity**.

Pupils improvising a scene from a play.

You may also wish to prepare some of the following publicity materials for your production:

- a theatre programme
- posters
- a newspaper advertisement
- a local radio trailer or cast interview
- photographic stills for the theatre foyer.

Stereotypes

> **Stereotype**: (verb) to assume that each individual person in a particular group of people will naturally possess certain characteristics.

We often have a fixed image of certain types of people which helps us to place them neatly in our minds. In order to explore the idea of stereotyping either brainstorm or make a list which includes everything you know about the following sorts of people.

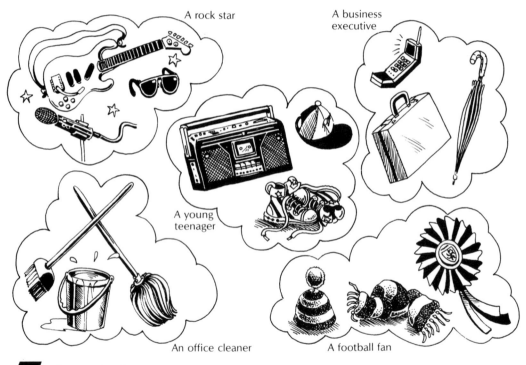

A rock star

A business executive

A young teenager

An office cleaner

A football fan

1   Report back

a)   In discussion groups pick out the details which appear on more than one list and note how many people have included a similar detail.

b)   Try to decide where your ideas about these people came from. Was it television, comics, newspapers, magazines, actual experience or something you have heard?

c)   If you find that your lists about a type of person are very different try to agree upon some of the reasons which have caused that difference.

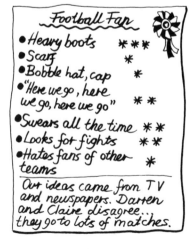

Football Fan
- Heavy boots   ✳ ✳ ✳
- Scarf   ✳
- Bobble hat, cap   ✳
- "Here we go, here we go, here we go"   ✳ ✳
- Swears all the time ✳ ✳
- Looks for fights   ✳ ✳
- Hates fans of other ✳ teams

Our ideas came from TV and newspapers. Darren and Claire disagree... they go to lots of matches.

Portrait Gallery

2 What stereotypes are portrayed in the pictures below?

We asked our artist to draw a portrait picture of what she thought Jammy Chivers would look like. She read *A Day In The Mind Of Tich Oldfield* and produced the following picture with explanations about her choice of features.

I drew Jammy Chivers like this because:

- His nickname made me think of teachers in comics like *The Beano* or *The Dandy*.
- He sounds old fashioned and, like the teachers in comics, I think he would wear a mortar-board cap and gown and carry a cane.
- He seems to be a boring teacher and I have tried to show this by standing him in front of a blackboard covered in historical facts. His jaw is long because he talks too much.
- I imagine he is a strict teacher but one who is laughed at behind his back.

3 Now it's your turn. Draw any character from one of the two plays and give reasons for your choices about that character's appearance.

4 Display your drawings in a class picture gallery and look out for those characters which seem to be the most stereotypical.

Challenging Stereotypes

1 Read the following extract from the beginning of Forrest Wilson's book *Super Gran Superstar*.

In small groups discuss the ways in which Super Gran seems different from the stereotypical image of an elderly woman.

2 a) Collect as many newspaper stories and articles about elderly people as you can find and share your cuttings with other members of the class.

   b) What image of aged people is presented in the press?

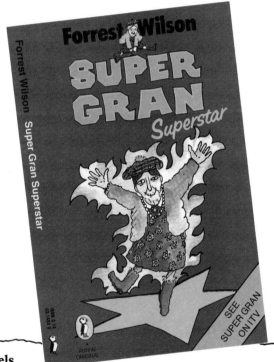

Meals on Wheels

Edison Faraday Black emerged from the supermarket to join her father, who had been waiting for her outside in his wheelchair.

'Look!' Mr Black exclaimed, pointing.

In the distance, but rapidly approaching them, careering down the High Street at full speed on a rusted, discarded skateboard, came a little old lady. She was dressed for the part in a bashed, tattered crash helmet and torn second-hand knee and elbow pads and she zigzagged in and out of the traffic.

She weaved her way across occupied zebra crossings, scattering cross crossers in every direction. She clanked on and off pavements and narrowly avoided the crowds of shoppers, mothers with prams, patrolling traffic wardens, policemen on point duty, buses, lorries, cars and cyclists. And in her hands she held a large stack of covered tin plates, balanced precariously one on top of the other, leaning like a tottering Tower of Pisa!

It was Super Gran!

As she approached Edison and Mr Black she whistled. And the girl and her father – and everyone else within earshot! – shot their fingers into their ears to prevent themselves being Super-deafened!

'Hello, Super Gran . . .' Edison waved to her old friend – who promptly waved back at her! 'No, Super Gran – don't wave! Your hands are full . . .!'

The girl closed her eyes, shuddered to think what would happen and waited to hear the expected crash of the tin-plated meals all over the street.

But, by some miracle, the crash never came. Somehow, with a nifty piece of Super-juggling, Super Gran managed to keep not only her *own* balance but also the balance of the teetering pile of plates, as she swept on down the High Street, scything a path through pedestrians, who hurriedly jumped out of her way, and traffic, which hastily braked to let her past.

'Is that her version of "Meals on Wheels"?' Edison's father asked, as Super Gran disappeared into the distance.

'Yes, *one* of them!' Edison laughed, as she pushed her father in his chair along the street.

Delivering Meals on Wheels was Super Gran's way of helping the town's old people, after feeling guilty about playing with her Super-powers instead of doing some good with them.

Ernie's Aunt becomes a similar character to Super Gran when Ernie imagines her taking on Kid Saracen at the fair.

3 Look at one of the two plays in this book and list the moments when a character seems to break away from, and challenge their more usual or stereotypical role.

4 Both plays show us how much fun it can be to challenge a stereotype. Create your own character who does not conform to a stereotype.

    a) Brainstorm your chosen stereotype and decide how your character will be different.

    b) Write the opening to a story which introduces your readers to this new character.

'Great Heavens, it's Tich Bond!'

1   Who decides that a particular person is a hero or heroine?

2   Create your own collage of heroes using photographic, cartoon or hand-drawn images.

3   In pairs discuss why people identify with heroes and heroines.

Reach for the Stars

1   You have been given the opportunity to interview the hero or heroine of your choice, what would you ask, how could you begin? These were the problems which faced 16-year-old Rachel Mealing from Stockport when she decided that she would like to write a magazine article about the pop singer, Sybil.

'At last, after weeks of relentlessly pestering the Press Officer at PWL Records I had finally achieved my goal, an interview with Sybil. I had heard her two hits, *Don't Take Me Over* and *Walk On By* and I became intrigued by the quality of her voice.

As the important day approached my anxiety grew along with a feeling of disbelief. Surely she would not bother to ring? My heart jumped at the sound of the telephone and I took a deep breath before lifting the receiver. A friendly American voice put me at ease. I was finally doing my first interview.

Since so little was known about Sybil in this country I had prepared a series of basic questions to provide background information about her family and early singing career. I wanted to produce an article which gave a good and complete impression of Sybil but I did not want to ask any questions which might cause offence. I planned my interview in four main parts; early life, religion, charity support and relationships. Once the interview was complete I painstakingly reduced the total number of words to five hundred and popped the article in the post.'

SYBIL – FROM CHOIRGIRL TO CHART TOPPER

One of America's premier female singers, Sybil has already had two smash hits in the United Kingdom with *Don't Take Me Over* and *Walk On By*. She has recently signed up with Stock Aitken Waterman and although her success seems relatively sudden, she is the first to point out that it results from years of hard work and rebuffs. Sybil sees her success as being self induced; her lifestyle following on from her struggle to get dance music accepted in the music industry. Using this argument Sybil justifies the amount of money received by someone of her status, and also points out that stardom is not her aim, but simply to be successful.

Sybil's early musical experience was singing gospel in a local church choir and religion still plays an important role in her life. Although not able to visit church as often as she would like, her faith is prevalent and she sees God as her guide, her blessings coming from Him. Her belief helps her to keep going in the demanding music world and to maintain a grip on reality. Sybil is very optimistic, believing that if you want something, and are prepared to really work at it, anything is possible.

When Sybil's talent was discovered her mother gave support straight away, but her father was less enthusiastic about her change of direction from law school and a secure future, to the notoriously unstable music business. Her parents

Who's in the News?

1   Choose the hero or heroine whom you would most like to interview. Decide upon an important occasion or event which might provide the reason for your interview and put your star personality back in the news headlines.

You will be given five minutes to conduct the interview so it is important that you consider the type of story you are looking for and prepare your questions carefully.

2   With a partner read through each other's questions and suggest any necessary changes which could make the interview more successful. Hold on to your partner's questions.

3   Now is your chance to be that hero! During the next five minutes your partner will be questioning you about your involvement in the current media event.

Improvise the interview with your partner and then swap the roles of hero and reporter. Reporters will need to keep notes or make a tape of the interview.

SUPERSTAR SAVES THE DAY

WEMBLEY WIZARD WOOS FANS ...

RETURN OF A HERO

BRILLIANT SOLO PERFORMANCE

LEGEND SHOCKS

SCOOP ...SCOOP ...SCOOP ...SCOOP ...SCOOP ...

4   In pairs select the interview which will provide the material for your news feature and produce one of the following:

a)   an article for the newspaper of your choice

b)   a radio news item

c)   a bulletin or news item for television.

The Secret Life of Walter Mitty

Literature and films often focus upon the world of characters like Tich and Ernie who lead a fantasy existence. One of the most famous of these characters is James Thurber's, Walter Mitty.

 Read the following extract and think about the ways in which the story switches between fantasy and reality to reveal Walter Mitty's secret life.

 Create your own secret life story switching between reality and the fantasy which is imagined in a character's mind.

'We're going through!' The Commander's voice was like thin ice breaking. He wore his full-dress uniform, with the heavily braided white cap pulled down rakishly over one cold grey eye. 'We can't make it, sir. It's spoiling for a hurricane, if you ask me.' 'I'm not asking you, Lieutenant Berg,' said the Commander. 'Throw on the power lights! Rev her up to 8,500! We're going through!' The pounding of the cylinders increased: ta-pocketa-pocketa-pocketa-*pocketa-pocketa*. The Commander stared at the ice forming on the pilot window. He walked over and twisted a row of complicated dials. 'Switch on No. 8 auxiliary!' he shouted. 'Switch on No. 8 auxiliary!' repeated Lieutenant Berg. 'Full strength in No. 3 turret!' shouted the Commander. 'Full strength in No. 3 turret!' The crew, bending to their various tasks in the huge, hurtling eight-engined Navy hydroplane, looked at each other and grinned. 'The Old Man'll get us through,' they said to one another. 'The Old Man ain't afraid of Hell!' . . .

'Not so fast! You're driving too fast!' said Mrs. Mitty. 'What are you driving so fast for?'

'Hmm?' said Walter Mitty. He looked at his wife, in the seat beside him, with shocked astonishment. She seemed grossly unfamiliar, like a strange woman who had yelled at him in a crowd. 'You were up to fifty-five,' she said. 'You know I don't like to go more than forty. You were up to fifty-five.' Walter Mitty drove on towards Waterbury in silence, the roaring of the SN202 through the worst storm in twenty years of Navy flying fading in the remote, intimate airways of his mind. 'You're tensed up again,' said Mrs. Mitty. 'It's one of your days. I wish you'd let Dr. Renshaw look you over.'

Walter Mitty stopped the car in front of the building where his wife went to have her hair done. 'Remember to get those overshoes while I'm having my hair done,' she said. 'I don't need overshoes,' said Mitty. She put her mirror back into her bag. 'We've been through all that,' she said, getting out of the car. 'You're not a young man any longer.' He raced the engine a little. 'Why don't you wear your gloves? Have you lost your gloves?' Walter Mitty reached in a pocket and brought out the gloves. He put them on, but after she had turned and gone into the building and he had driven on to a red light, he took them off again. 'Pick it up, brother!' snapped a cop as the lights changed, and Mitty hastily pulled on his gloves and lurched ahead. He drove round the streets aimlessly for a time, and then he drove past the hospital on his way to the parking lot.

. . . 'It's the millionaire banker, Wellington McMillan,' said the pretty nurse. 'Yes?' said Walter Mitty, removing his gloves slowly. 'Who has the case?' 'Dr. Renshaw and Dr. Benbow, but there are two specialists here, Dr. Remington from New York and Mr. Pritchard-Mitford from London. He flew over.' A door opened down a long, cool corridor and Dr. Renshaw came out. He looked distraught and haggard. 'Hello, Mitty,' he said. 'We're having the devil's own time with McMillan, the millionaire banker and close personal friend of Roosevelt. Obsterosis of the ductal tract. Tertiary. Wish you'd take a look at him.' 'Glad to,' said Mitty.